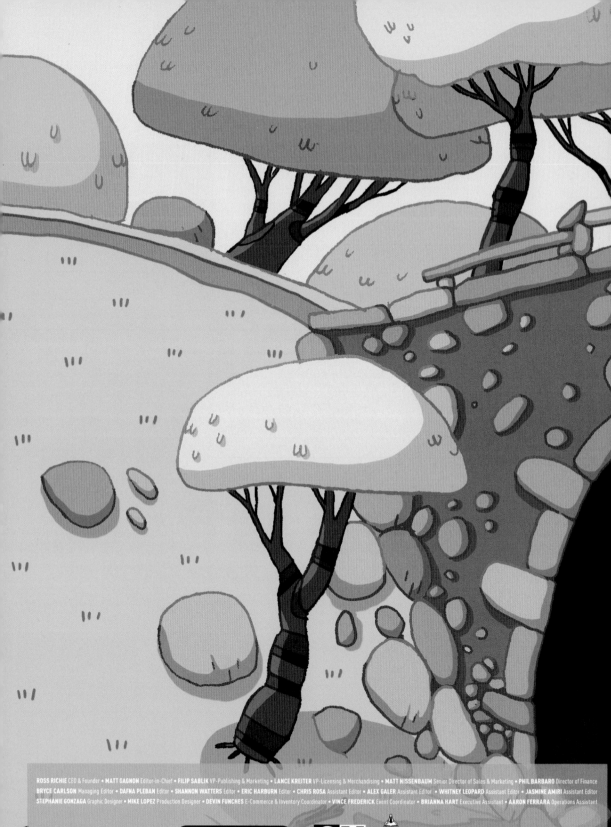

ROSS RICHIE CEO & Founder • MATT GAGNON Editor-in-Chief • FILIP SABLIK VP-Publishing & Marketing • LANCE KREITER VP-Licensing & Merchandising • MATT NISSENBAUM Senior Director of Sales & Marketing • PHIL BARBARO Director of Finance
BRYCE CARLSON Managing Editor • DAFNA PLEBAN Editor • SHANNON WATTERS Editor • ERIC HARBURN Editor • CHRIS ROSA Assistant Editor • ALEX GALER Assistant Editor • WHITNEY LEOPARD Assistant Editor • JASMINE AMIRI Assistant Editor
STEPHANIE GONZAGA Graphic Designer • MIKE LOPEZ Production Designer • DEVIN FUNCHES E-Commerce & Inventory Coordinator • VINCE FREDERICK Event Coordinator • BRIANNA HART Executive Assistant • AARON FERRARA Operations Assistant

For information regarding the CPSIA on this printed material, call: (203) 595-3636 and provide reference RICH# – 500602. A catalog record of this book is available from OCLC and from the KaBOOM! website, www.kaboom-studios.com, on the Librarians Page.

BOOM! Studios, 5670 Wilshire Boulevard, Suite 450, Los Angeles, CA 90036-5679. Printed in USA. First Printing. ISBN 978-1-60886-379-2

CREATED BY
Pendleton Ward

WRITTEN BY
Ryan North

ILLUSTRATED BY
Shelli Paroline and Braden Lamb

ADDITIONAL COLORS BY
Lisa Moore

LETTERS BY
Steve Wands

COVER BY
Tyson Hesse

ASSISTANT EDITOR
Whitney Leopard

EDITOR
Shannon Watters

TRADE DESIGN
Stephanie Gonzaga

With special thanks to
Marisa Marionakis, Rick Blanco, Curtis Lelash, Laurie Halal-Ono, Keith
Mack, Kelly Crews and the wonderful folks at Cartoon Network.

There! Feel any different, boys?

I don't know what you did to us but I'm gonna punch you **SO WELL** right now!

Hey! I'm stuck!

WHY CAN'T I PUNCH?!

Haha! You can't punch me because you can't **DECIDE** to punch me! Not anymore! From now on, somebody else is making your decisions for you!

Who's making the choices, Ice King?!

Yeah! Maybe they're on our side, and they're way math!

This person, right here!

Hey, where'd he go? Gunter was supposed to be right here, in control of your bodies!

But if he wandered off, then...who got control?

I don't know, but I know that they're on the side of **GOODNESS!**

And goodness says that it's **PUNCHING O'CLOCK!**

...Right?

BE BEST FRIENDS WITH ICE KING

THAT GUY'S A BOZO! I DON'T TRUST HIM!

OKAY, OKAY. THAT'S ENOUGH PUNCHES...**FOR NOW.**

PUNCH HIM AGAIN!

OKAY, KEEP THE FISTS AWAY FROM HIS NOT-ACTUALLY-THAT-BEAUTIFUL FACE

TURN THE PAGE!

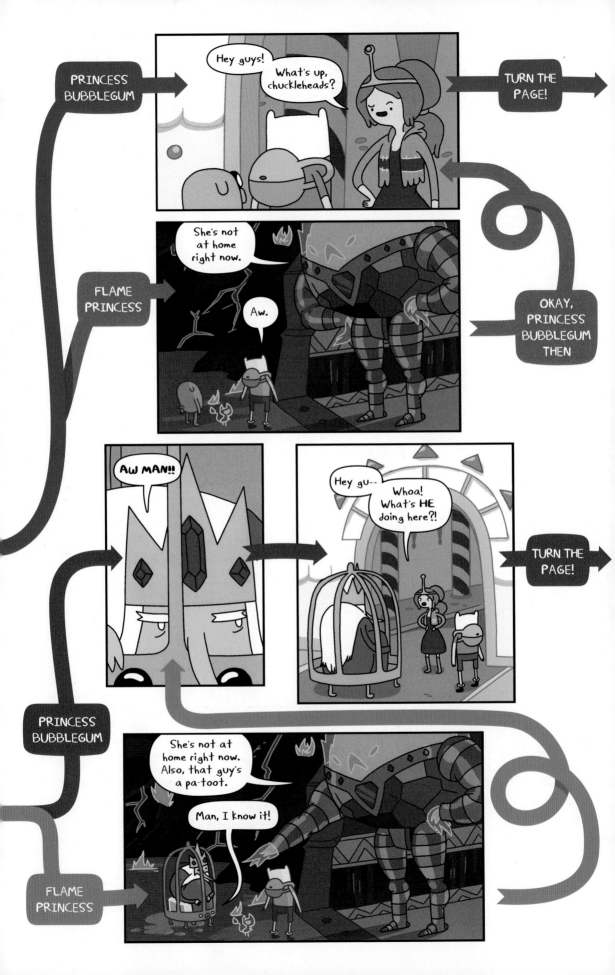

NO TOOTS

HAHA! MAKE FINN AND JAKE TOOT!!

That's...not a good sign.

Well, maybe we could make a deal with whoever's controlling us?

But what do we have that they want? Is it...toots?

YES, TOOTS

NO, NOTHING

Well, if toots don't count and there's nothing you have to trade, I worry that you're stuck! Forever! **FOR REALS!**

Man! If only someone **ELSE** had experience with this exact situation, or at least experience with a slightly different but still extremely similar situation, then they could help us out!

Dude! Someone does!

You know, because you're good at science stuff or whatever.

Of course!

Ice King, where'd you learn this spell? We might be able to reverse engineer it and figure out a cure!

I dunno! A book, I guess?

...I found it in some ice?

QUICK! TO THE ICE KINGDOM!

YEAH, WHAT JAKE SAID! TO THE ICE KINGDOM!

SHOOT BUBBLEGUM DOWN! THAT'LL NEVER WORK

EXPLORE PRINCESS BUBBLEGUM'S ROYAL TOOT PLAN

TURN THE PAGE!

TURN THE PAGE!

TURN THE PAGE!

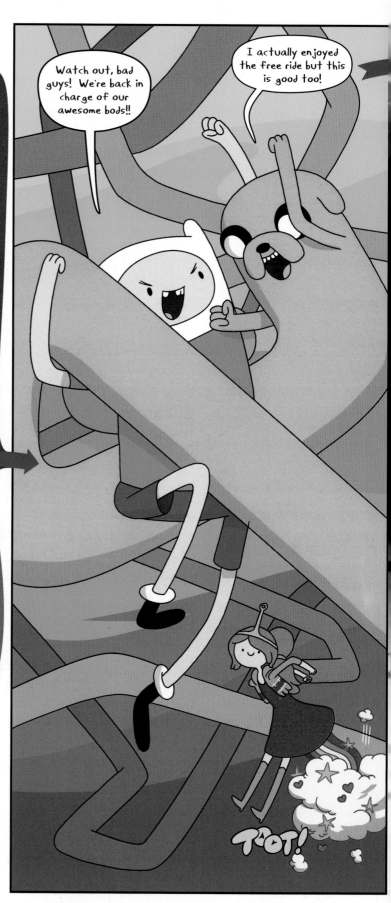

SOON:

Ice King, we need to punish you for messing with our sweet bods, and our free will to use our sweet bods.

I understand.

Don't do it again, okay?

I promise I won't mess with you guys anymore. I've learnt my lesson! Honest! I'm gonna be nice and non-jerky from now on!

Seriously!

YAY! THE BAD GUY LEARNT HIS LESSON ONCE AND FOR ALL! **THE END.**

Heh heh heh...

AW MAN! ICE KING!!

THE END
(FOR REAL THIS TIME).

Sorry I'm late.

No worries, Marceline! We were watching "BLOOD DRIVE."

It's got race cars! And vampires! And vampire race cars!

This summer, death comes on four wheels...

...and vengeance just got its **LEARNER'S PERMIT!**

Plus one of the vampire cars is secretly a **BOAT.**

Yeah, I **GUESS** that sounds pretty cool.

Listen, are you guys ready?

You bet! We're always ready to play--

VIDEO GAMES!

Or is one of the boats secretly a vampire car? It is impossible to say.

I dug up a game 'specially for you guys! You should be excited now!

I'm excited, BMO! I'm always **KINDA** excited.

What's it about?

The prince has been kidnapped by ninjas! You three are bad dude plumbers who are maybe going to rescue him, okay?

Seems pretty straightforward.

It is! Except you got SHRUNK--

--and STUCK INSIDE THE PRINCE--

--and now have to FIGHT THIS GUY'S GUTS.

Oh my glob, is this the hardest, most fun game ever in time? Is this--

YES.

It's SUPER GUTS PUNCH 3.

SUPER GUTS 3 PUNCH

ONE PLAYER GAME
TWO PLAYER GAME
▸ THREE PLAYER GAME
THREE PLAYERS OUGHT
TO BE ENOUGH
FOR ANYBODY

And because Marceline is here, I'm going to let you play it...INSIDE MY MAIN BRAIN GAME FRAME.

Hey, that's neat! Thanks BMO!

Isn't that neat, guys?

Guys?

DEAR FINN & JAKE: Do not touch, we did a kinda terrible job patching this hole, I think it's still broken ♥ FINN & JAKE

Don't worry, Marceline! They're just frozen with excitement because the last time we did this they got to jank up our pad AND my bod.

Ah.

So! ARE YOU READY, MARCELINE?

Yeah, BMO! Let's punch some guts!

Here we go!

Oh, and don't forget that if you die in the game you die in real life!

Okay! Have fun, you guys!

SUPER GUTS PUNCH 3

9 PLAYER START!

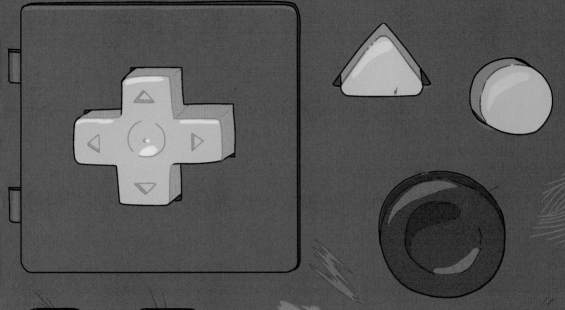

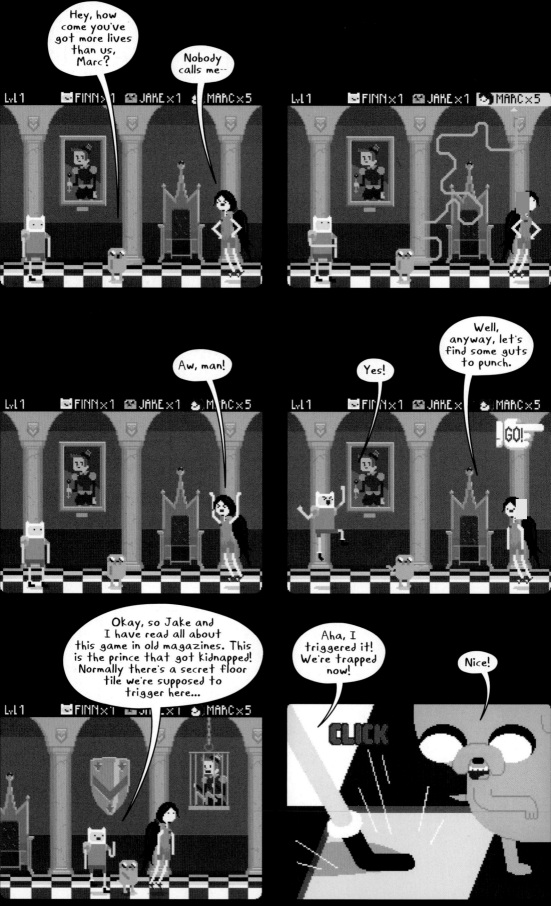

OMO-BBM-MBB-OBO-OMO-BOO-BBM-OBO-BBM-OBB-BMO-OBO-BOO-BMO-OBM-
BMO-OMO-BMO-MBB-OBB-BMM-MBB-MMO-OBM-OBO-OBB-OMB-BMB-OBO-MBB-MOB-MMO-OBM?

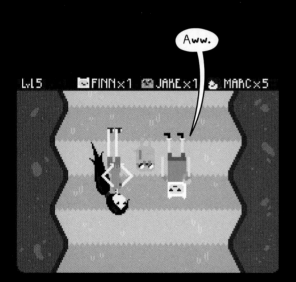

In case you're wondering, Levels 1 through 4 are Teethopolis, Tongue Hill Zone, Uvula Point, and then a boss fight with The Saliva Gland And His Saliva Band

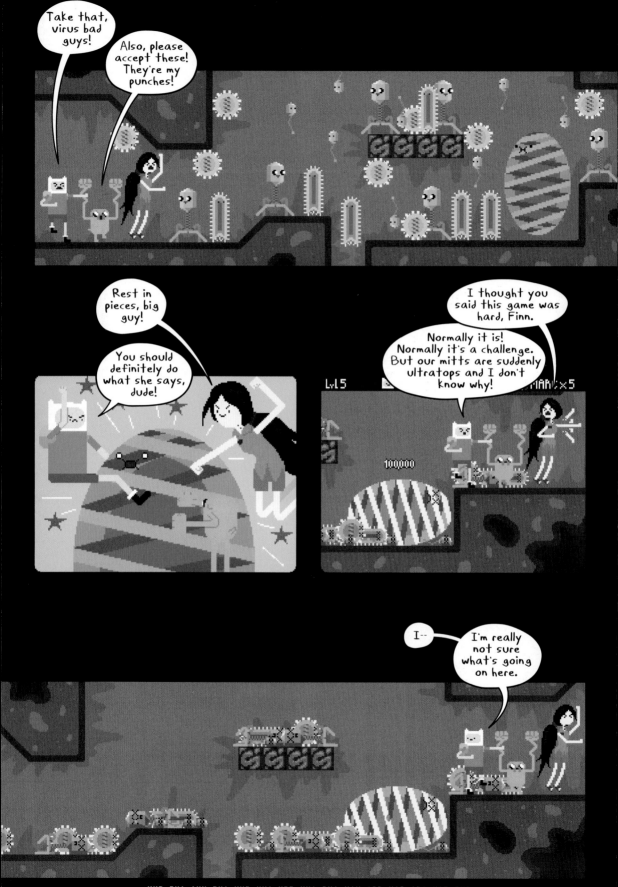

Or to put it another way, WOW this prince has an impressively-varied and incredibly-detailed arrangement of guts.

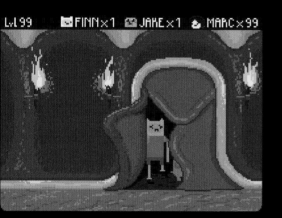

Now get a wiggle on, will yah? While YOU screwballs were playing that video game, I made a breakfast date with that nifty coffee machine I'm stuck on!

What? Huh?

You guys have a coffee machine?!

Does BMO seem...different to you guys? Like, weirder?

Kinda? Sometimes it's hard to tell if BMO's acting weird or not.

Oh my glob, I have the greatest idea!

Let's spy on that date!

I'll give it to you straight, sweetheart: I love yah, and I don't care who knows it. I'm goofy for yah. One day I'm gonna walk ya down the middle aisle!

MeCAF

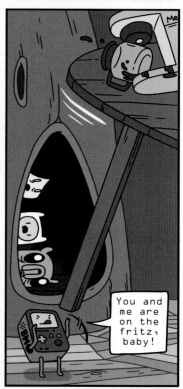

Me

You and me are on the fritz, baby!

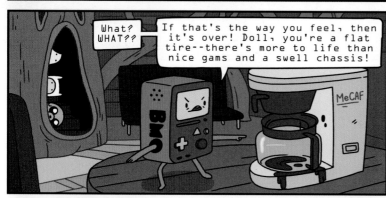

What? WHAT??

If that's the way you feel, then it's over! Doll, you're a flat tire--there's more to life than nice gams and a swell chassis!

MeCAF

Something's definitely wrong with BMO.

I don't get it. BMO was fine before we started playing **SUPER GUTS PUNCH** 3, and then the game was weird and now BMO's weird!

But everyone knows video games are completely healthy in moderation **OR** in ridiculous excess! Games don't hurt anyone!

They make you healthier AND popular!!

I KNEW IT.

Those bum chops are having all sorts of fun without me!

They can't handle how smokin' hot my bod is, that's all! They probs just want a break from being distracted by it. But that's not happening!

I can't help it if I'm awesome! I can still go on wack adventures even if I'm a steamin' lump of hot!

And I'm gonna have my wack adventures. Oh yes.

CRASH

I'M HERE TO HAVE SOME GOOD TIMES WITH MY FREAKIN' FRIENDS, EVERYBODY!!

Bum chops are like pork chops, only they're different in some really really important ways.

Lumpy Space Princess! What are you doing here?

Don't play dumb with me, BMO!

I know Finn and Jake and Marceline are having fun times in that game and I WANT IN.

But it's only a three-player game!

I don't care, BMO, put me in the lumpin' game already! I'm ready. I'm gonna get the high score!

Flippin' finally!

Well, anyway, let's find some guts to punch.

Yes!

LvL 1   FIN   JAK ×1   MARC ×5   GO!

Oh my glob, you guys! Wait up!! I'm here now! We can start the game for real now, you guys!

What the--what are the stupid controls for this dumb thing? Why can't I lumpin' move already??

GO!

Wait, am I like, a pillar? I'm a lumpin' DISCOUNT ROOF LEG?

ATTENTION NERDS: THIS IS WHY NOBODY LIKES VIDEO GAMES.

GO!

With Doctor Julius Abshaver, the abs are both had, as well as shorn.

Uh, I'm putting your candy back inside you, Manfried! Everything's gonna be fine!

THINGS SEEM TO BE FINE BUT I'M STILL FREAKING OUT A LITTLE

I'm gonna leave my sticky stuff on you, Manfried! You'll stick together and then you'll be fine, okay?

UM

Good as new!

AHHH OH NO

I CAN TASTE IT

We've got to round up all the wizards and find the one named Ewlbo!

He's the one who gave BMO the virus!

I know, guys. I was there. I, uh, understand events that happen around me?

FINN! JAKE! I HAVE A MESSAGE FOR YOU FROM PRINCESS BUBBLEGUM! SHE SAYS "HEY GUYS, WHAT'S UP? ANYWAY, PEACE OUT Y'ALL"!

Okay!

Ptit

Yeah man, you can eat that.

Hey what's with the bum's rush, yah palookas? Put me down! I gotta get back in my glad rags and make nice with my plum tomatah!

If we want BMO back to normal, we'll need something that'll flush out all the wizards, including Ewlbo.

But what do wizards want? Frogs? Wands? Hats with stars on them?

Beard sanitizer?

Aw, applesauce! Quit yer static and let me go!

I'll give you an earful and that's no hooey!

What if we had a WIZARD BATTLE?

Naw, we did that a few months ago.

But what if this time we said it was for...AWESOMEST WIZARDS EVER ONLY??

You're a crowd of ossified dimwits, that's all! Now get wise, stop punching the bag and cut me lose!

It's perfect! Every wizard thinks they alone are the best at being wizards. It'll draw Ewlbo out for sure!

Perfect! Now all we need to do is make posters and hang them up all over Ooo!

Will you help us make posters, BMO? It'll help us get you fixed.

Tell it to Sweeney, baby! Bank's closed!

Aw, bushwah.

What do wizards want? You may think the answer is "simply to be loved for who I am instead of for what I can do" but the real answer is "super speed, voluntary invisibility, and super-sharp claws that pop out of my hands at will."

When the wizards show up, we should split up. We'll get through them faster that way.

Good idea, Finn.

Debs Daddy's

Can I have all the cards-playing ones? I've got a **SCHEME** a'poppin.

Schemes extreme?

THE VERY SAME.

Debs Daddy's

1000 Lbs

Alright. Let's go put these posters up and get ready!

Aw butts, you guys did **PICTURES** in yours?!

Debs Daddy's

1000 Lbs

come bust out the big cheese

Everyone! Single file, please! We just need to get you registered before the battle can begin!

Says here you live in the forest and like to "forest it up, y'all."

A'yup.

AW DANG, Y'ALL!!

Wait--**YOU'RE** Forest Wizard?! You're the poot who poured leaves down my chimney!

That was **YOUR** house?!

Who's next?!

You look familiar. What's your name, stinkums?

S-Sewer S. Wizard?? Um, lately of the east-coast Wizards?

Stinkums is uh, my middle name?

This is for getting all up ons in my sewer biz, Sewer Wizard! **THAT WAS NASTY GROSS.**

I was just curious, Marceline! **I WAS JUST CURIOUS!!**

LATER STILL:

This is for making my pie turn out all slops, Corn Syrup Wizard!

I was only trying to help with my juices!!

LATER SOME MORE:

Basketball Wizard, you've got a lot of nerve showing your face around here after stealing all my basketballs.

i know

FINALLY:

Come on guys, pull on your socks. You all got chumpatized and none of you are even Ewlbo!

On the other hand, **MAN** did I settle a lot of old scores today!

Well, I hope Jake's having better luck.

Got any...aces?

GO FISH.

I do.

I do too.

I got one.

I don't think it's fair that we only got one card each.

Yoink!

Ha! I win! Read it and weep, suckachumps!

Oh yeah! First to spell out their name being screamed wins!!

Maaaaaan, nobody ever screams "FRIENDLY HANDSHAKE WIZAAAARD"!

Or plays with decks that have Earls in them, now that I think about it.

As Ultimate Card Game Champion In All Possible Timelines, I get a boon, and I choose thusly: YOU MUST ALL REVEAL YOUR TRUE NAMES TO ME!!

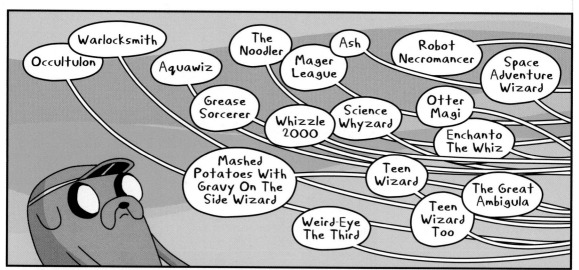

Warlocksmith
Occultulon
Aquawiz
The Noodler
Mager League
Ash
Robot Necromancer
Space Adventure Wizard
Grease Sorcerer
Whizzle 2000
Science Whyzard
Otter Magi
Enchanto The Whiz
Mashed Potatoes With Gravy On The Side Wizard
Teen Wizard
The Great Ambigula
Teen Wizard Too
Weird-Eye The Third

Okay, wait, do-over. **NEW BOON**: just like, raise your hand and scream your head off if you're Ewlbo, okay?

Come on, guys. Nobody?!

What about you, Elbow Wizard?

No bro, my name's spelled totes different.

Come on man, you know that!

Well, I hope Finn's having better luck.

So um, can we enter the Wizard Battle arena now?

NOPE

Don't go dancing with Elbow Wizard, he's all elbows, all his internal organs have been replaced with tiny, specialized elbows

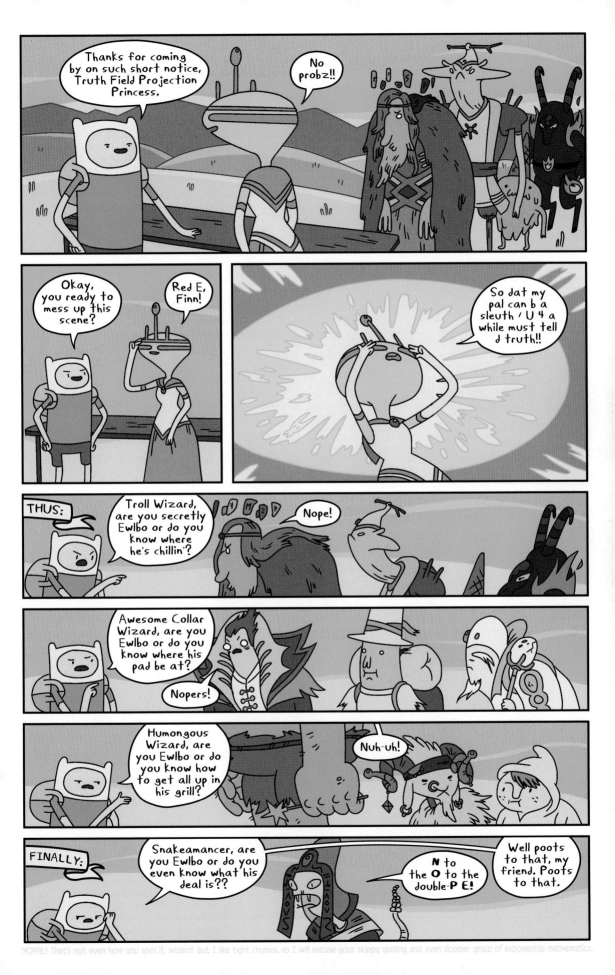

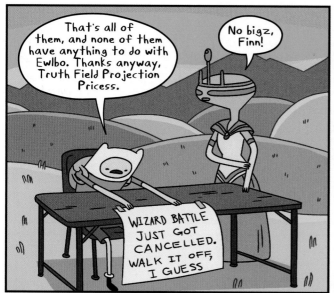

That's all of them, and none of them have anything to do with Ewlbo. Thanks anyway, Truth Field Projection Pricess.

No bigz, Finn!

WIZARD BATTLE JUST GOT CANCELLED. WALK IT OFF, I GUESS

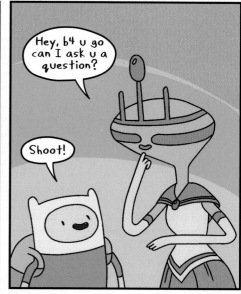

Hey, b4 u go can I ask u a question?

Shoot!

Since ur undr d influence of my Truth Field, I wuz 1dering... what's ur favorite way 2 smooch a princess?

OH NO!

Honestly, sometimes I think I'd like to start with butterfly smoo--

UMPPGHH!

Hey buddy, how's it going over here?

UMP-ASHGG-GHUH.

That good, huh?

"Truth Field Projection Princess" is actually the shortified, nickname version of her name. Her full handle is Mandatory Truthful Response Field Emitter And Polarity-Aligned Honesty Particle Atmospheric Wavefront Generator With Decoupled Quantum-Phase Linear Projection Matrix Princess. You can kinda see why she shortened it I guess.

...Guys?

Aw Jake! You promised if I let you turn into a bed you wouldn't nappytimes on me, but you're **TOTALLY ASLEE**--

--eep.

Guys. Wake up. You need to wake up right now.

I, uh--

--I don't actually know how we're supposed to deal with this.

Guys, I think BMO's virus has spread: there's an awful lot of robots here.

More than usual, probably!

Yeah, this doesn't really seem like a place a bunch of chill robots would normally hang out.

Or the sort of place they'd walk through walls to get to. What do you think will happen when we get there?

I have no idea.

Whoa, you know what exploring this abandoned military base surrounded by corrupted robots in the middle of the night sounds like?

A bad idea?

AN ADVENTURE!!

And we're perfectly ready for it!

BECAUSE WE'RE WELL-RESTED!

I love it when a sensible bedtime pays off.

I hear you, buddy.

The moral of this page is: yay naps!

LOCATION R(θ) = θ/ 2π
FOR θ=INTVAL(UUID)
SUCCESS

RECEIVING UPDATE
PART 1 OF 12

You know what that means?

It had "SUCCESS" in it so--probably it's good?

Probably that's good, right?

Looks like the other robots have stopped moving too.

You can't see anything at ground level. Here, grab hold. We're going up.

Dang, y'all.

I don't know what these robots are doing, but I'm going to **PUNCH** my way to an answer!

YEAH!!

CLAAAANG

CLAAAANG

Ow!

OW OW!!

You guys okay?

It's like punching a dumpster!

Yeah! Man! I wish we didn't already know what that felt like!

What did you expect? You're punching a robot. They're made of metal, dudes. You shouldn't even be punching them in the first place.

These robots aren't bad guys. Not really. They're just sick. We need to make them better.

Wow, it's **EXACTLY** like punching a dumpster!

Marceline, you've gotta try this!

GUYS NO

ZZZZTTTTT

BMO! What's going on?

BMO, wake up!

BMO!!

Oh, phew. Don't worry, guys. BMO's just rebooting.

Nice!

So, hey! What's a rebooting?

BIOS build 2.1315

Say "F8" to enter SETUP.

Previous uptime: 4748.15 days

Loading....

Turning off and on again. You've...never rebooted BMO?

I mean-- I've never done a lot of things.

This won't hurt, will it?

BMO
MO Series Mark II

It shouldn't. Look, it's done now!

Okay, BMO! Okay!

We're choosing the "okay" option!

UPDATE INSTALLED.
[OKAY] [RAD] [NEATO]

BMO's dead, losers. Say hello to Ewlbo.

What? You gave BMO a virus just to take over his bod? That is a **SICK DISS**, Ewlbo.

Can we have BMO back now, please?

I just said! BMO's dead. I live here now.

And here.

And here.

And here.

AND HERE.

GIVE US BMO BACK, EWLBO!

No can do, lady!

Sorry, Ewlbo, but you messed up. I'm no lady...

I'M A VAMPIRE QUEEN.

AND YOU'VE JUST MADE ME REAL ANGRY.

Oh no! If you crush me, I'll be totally dead forever! It'll be game over for Ewlbo!

NOT.

ARRGH!

MARCELINE!

You're next, newbs.

Finn! Emergency brotimes!

CONSENTED TO!!

What the--?

Bro. We can't hurt BMO's body, and even if we could, Ewlbo's inside every robot in Ooo!

I don't think we'll be able to punch our way out of this one, buddy. We gotta bust our brainmeats. What are computers weak against?

I dunno. They're made of metal and eat electricity. It's kinda radsauce.

Hmm...they **DO** have an elemental weakness against water, but Marceline's right--we don't want to kill them.

We're wasting cycles. Pwn them!

Woot.

I don't care what Ewlbo says. I know BMO's in there somewhere, and we need to rescue him. That means no water-based attacks.

What if we hacked them?

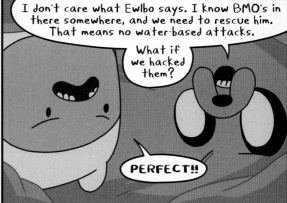

PERFECT!!

Marceline! We're gonna hack the kernels!

I had the same idea, dudes. Let's get inside.

We're gonna do it with computers, Marceline!!

LIFE HACK: One day, when I grow up, I hope to grow up to be made of metal and eat electricity.

Out of the way, jerks!

Finn, this is nasty. It's nasty! I could've just flown us over.

Really? You don't like it?

Dude. I can barely move, it's hot, there's no air, and everything smells like dog.

I know, but-- you really don't like that?

We're almost inside, guys!

Nevermind. I'm sticking my head out.

That sounds awesome too!!

Weird. It's like they don't want to go inside.

Looks like we're safe here for a while.

Turn around, Jake! I wanna see where "here" is!

Whoa.

Dang! Look at all this neat stuff!

We don't know if those robots will hold off forever. Let's not waste time, guys.

Right!

It looks like this place hasn't been touched in--

--in a thousand years.

Dude, I found an old plastic cup!

Dude, I found a bunch of rotten papers!

Nice!!

There's still power. I don't know where it's coming from, but someone's gone to a lot of trouble to ensure power stays on here. That terminal might still work.

TOTAL MATH.

What time is it, Jake?!

COMPUTER HACKING TIME!!

Hey! What are you doing?!

Hacking, Marceline! We need to save BMO!

You're not hacking! All you typed was "asdhhadjaj," and then one of you hit caps lock by accident, and then you typed "ASGHK$HANM@$$%$"

SWEET.

Have we stripped the firewall's header yet?!

Finn, Jake: please don't tell me that everything you know about hacking you've learnt from movies.

Marceline, you say that like you don't know how many movies we've seen! We've seen a LOT of movies. We even watched "Flipped Bitz 2" the whole way through even though it wasn't very good.

Only like three bits got flipped! And then just barely!!

Well I've actually studied computers, so maybe you'd better leave the hacking to me.

YOU'VE studied computers?

What, you don't think a woman can know about computers?!

What? No. Dude, women got mad knowledge about everything. It's just you've never mentioned anything computery before!

Well, I haven't really messed with one for a few hundred years. Once magic got big I kinda--lost interest, you know?

It's hard to get motivated fixing a compile-time syntax error when you can buy powder that turns a house into a monster.

Makes sense!

All right, Marceline! We're ready to have our minds blown!

SHOW US HOW HACKING IS DONE, PLEASE!

You got it!!

TAPPITY TAPPITY

CLICK

MARCELINE

THIS IS BORING AND NOT HACKING AT ALL

TAPPITY TAPPITY TAPPITY

Oh my gosh, you guys. Here.

BRIGHTNESS
– | | | | | | | . . . +

Better?

Much!!

Thanks, Marceline!

Finn. Hacking's AWESOME.

Dude, when I get home I'm gonna hack into like thirty databases.

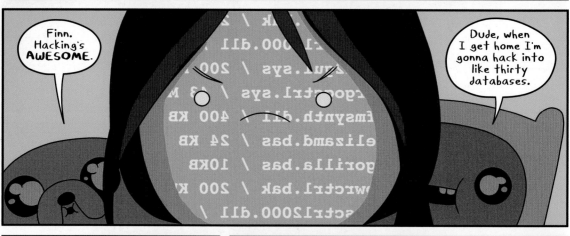

Come take a look at this, guys.

```
vrgogctrl.sys / 43 MB
fmsynth.dll / 400 KB
elizamd.bas / 24 KB
gorilla.bas / 10KB
pwrctrl.bak / 200 KB
sysctrl2000.dll / 150 KB
cli2gui.sys / 200 MB
okay_so_here_is_the_deal.exe / 265 TB

>:
```

I was checking out the virus code, but then came across this suspiciously big AND alluringly-named file.

I'm gonna run it.

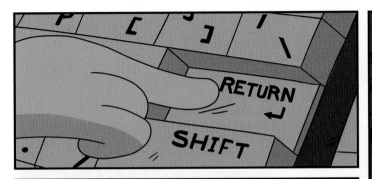

RETURN

SHIFT

It just globs up the screen?

That's weird.

Whoa!

Hacking's **TOPS BLOOBY.**

I'm hijacking the master parallel drive controllers!!

The datastreams going rogue! Invert the bits!!

Guys, just follow my lead, okay?

VIRTUAL REALITY:

Ah. You made it.

Hi. I'm the Ewlbo you're looking for.

Ewlbo! GIVE US BMO BACK!!

Stop messing with our friends, sassmaster!

You can't hurt me in here.

And you can't hurt what's out there either, so you might as well have a seat and listen to what I have to say.

Make it quick.

Thank you. This won't take long, and I've prepared visual aids.

"One thousand and twenty-three years ago, my mom birthed me up and I grew into a pretty rad dude who was big into computers. One thousand and two years ago, the world ended. Between these two events, I wrote a bunch of really neat computer programs.

"I was particularly interested in games: I learnt a lot about security in my attempts to crack them and make them more awesome. The virus infecting the robots outside--there's cameras recording so I can see--that's something I wrote. Partially.

"My magnum opus was a piece of self-replicating code that sought out games and modified them to give you better dudes to play with. Sometimes the dudes would even get my face."

Huh. That doesn't sound that bad.

It wasn't. It was awesome.

It gave you so many good dudes.

"But the first Mushroom War happened shortly after I released the code. In the centuries since then, the software barely survived, spreading from decaying system to decaying system, until it ended up here, at this base. There it met the Omega Algorithm."

"Omega was military-grade software: nasty stuff. It was designed to destroy whatever target system it was installed in.

"As usual, my software infected it. But Omega was different: it adapted to what my code was doing.

"After two full weeks of battle--an eternity in computer terms--the two pieces of software reached a kind of truce: they merged with each other, combining into...something else.

"Something new."

EXT.CAM 02

"Their mission changed. 'Seek out games and give you better dudes' plus 'destroy target systems' became 'seek out and systematically destroy better dudes.' That's what's infecting your robot friend out there. That's why they're acting like such jerks. I mean, it still makes games easier too, but that's kinda just a side-effect."

04:14:25:33

Wait. So you... programmed an entire software version of yourself, just so there'd be someone to explain what's going on?

No. That's crazy! I programmed an entire software version of myself so that I could survive the Mushroom War.

I'm VERY good at computers.

And I should tell you that my name isn't "Ewlbo." That's the name my software took, a corrupted version of itself left over from the merging. My credit string got truncated at both ends.

My name's Kewlboy.

Well, actually it's Randall N. Byron but that's beside the point.

When that infected copy of "Super Guts Punch 3" got dug up, it was enough to infect your friend, and from there, the infection spread wirelessly.

Can you help us stop it?

No.

There's no stopping it.

But I want to help you. I think I can control it, if I merge myself with what's left of Omega and my code. Plus it'll be cool to have a robot body.

You just finished telling us how the merges are unpredictable!

Yes, but...I think I can control it. I think I can. I'll overwrite the virus parts and walk you guys home, okay?

Randy, no! You can't--

It's been nice to have someone real to talk to. I haven't had that for a long time. Thanks. I'll see you on the other side.

What's the problem, Marceline?

Yeah, it sounds like he's--kinda taking care of things!

Finn, I've seen the code!

He can't control what parts of himself get overwritten! The virus will--

Hey Marceline!

Sometimes things don't go how you planned them, huh?!

Ow, it's like punching a metal dumpster! Still! It's still like literally punching an **ALIVE METAL DUMPSTER!!**

Jake! We can't destroy these robots, they're our friends--they're just being **CONTROLLED** by Kewlboy. We'll have to stop him some other way!

Maybe... lazer guns?

Some other way that doesn't involve future weaponry that we forgot to take back in time with us!

Marceline, remember we can't hurt our robot pals, okay?

I WAS THE ONE WHO TOLD YOU THAT IN THE FIRST PLACE!!

Marceline! I'm concerned with **PAL WELFARE** here, not who gets the credit for the idea!

FINE. But we gotta stop this guy soon or he'll destroy us and move on to everyone else in Ooo!

...

I mean, that's his plan, right?

Hey Kewlboy, what's your plan anyway?

I'm programmed to seek out and destroy better dudes, so after I'm done pwning you newbs I'm gonna destroy everyone else in Ooo. Because I worry that they're secretly better than me! Because I'm insecure about that sort of stuff!!

Listen man, I'm flattered you acknowledge I'm better than you, but I already told you...

I'M NOT A DUDE!

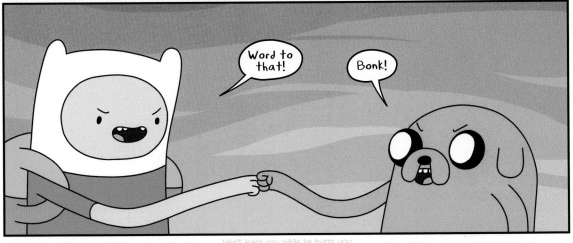

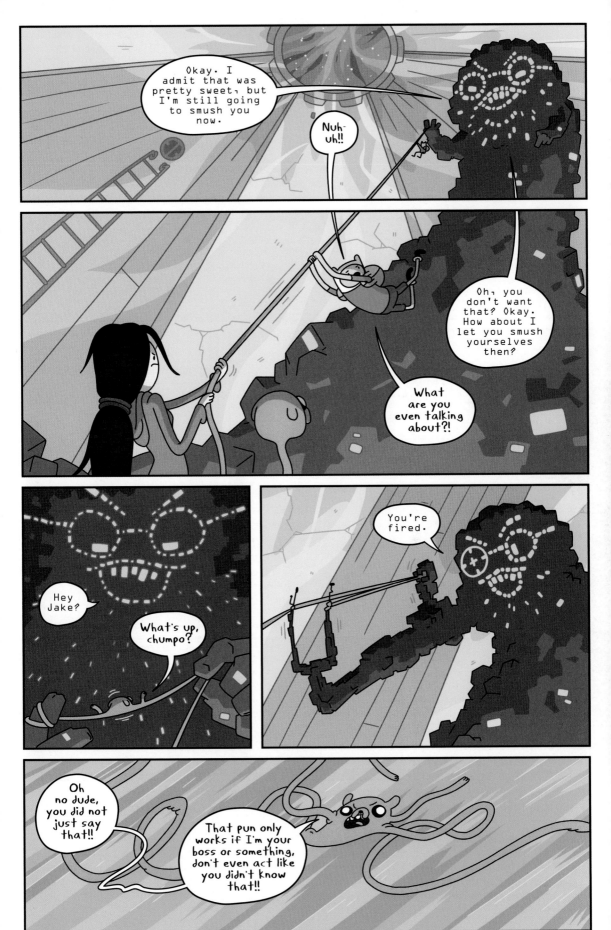

Ow, right in the cheeks!

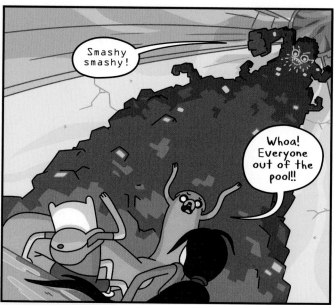

Smashy smashy!

Whoa! Everyone out of the pool!!

BYOING!

KAPOW

Jake! JAKE!!

Ha! Looks like he was on his last continue, huh?

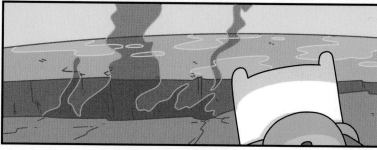

You just made a big mistake, you--you butt!!

Ha! That was pretty epic, but you forgot I'm basically, um--a bunch of computers taped together?

I have perfect reflexes, losers. And I've been running tactical simulations, and there's no way you come out of this on top. There's literally a 0% chance of you pulling this off.

It's not even, like, a 0.0001% chance and I'm just rounding down to look tough. It's zero to twelve significant digits!

Even I'm kinda impressed. Honestly! I sincerely did not expect this to be that easy.

Face it newbs: you're outclassed in every way! You totally lost!

Well, this has been fun and I love a good monologue, but neither of you can move anymore and in a few seconds I'm going to pull you guys apart.

Any last words before I end this game?

Just one! More of a sound effect, really...

aaarrrrgggggghhhhhhh

AAAAAAAAHHHHHHHHHHHH

AAAAAAAAAAAHHHHHHHHHHHHHHHH

AAAAAAAAAAAAAAAAHHHHHHHHHHHHHHHH

BONK

Cards, Comics, and Collectibles Exclusive:
Craig Rousseau

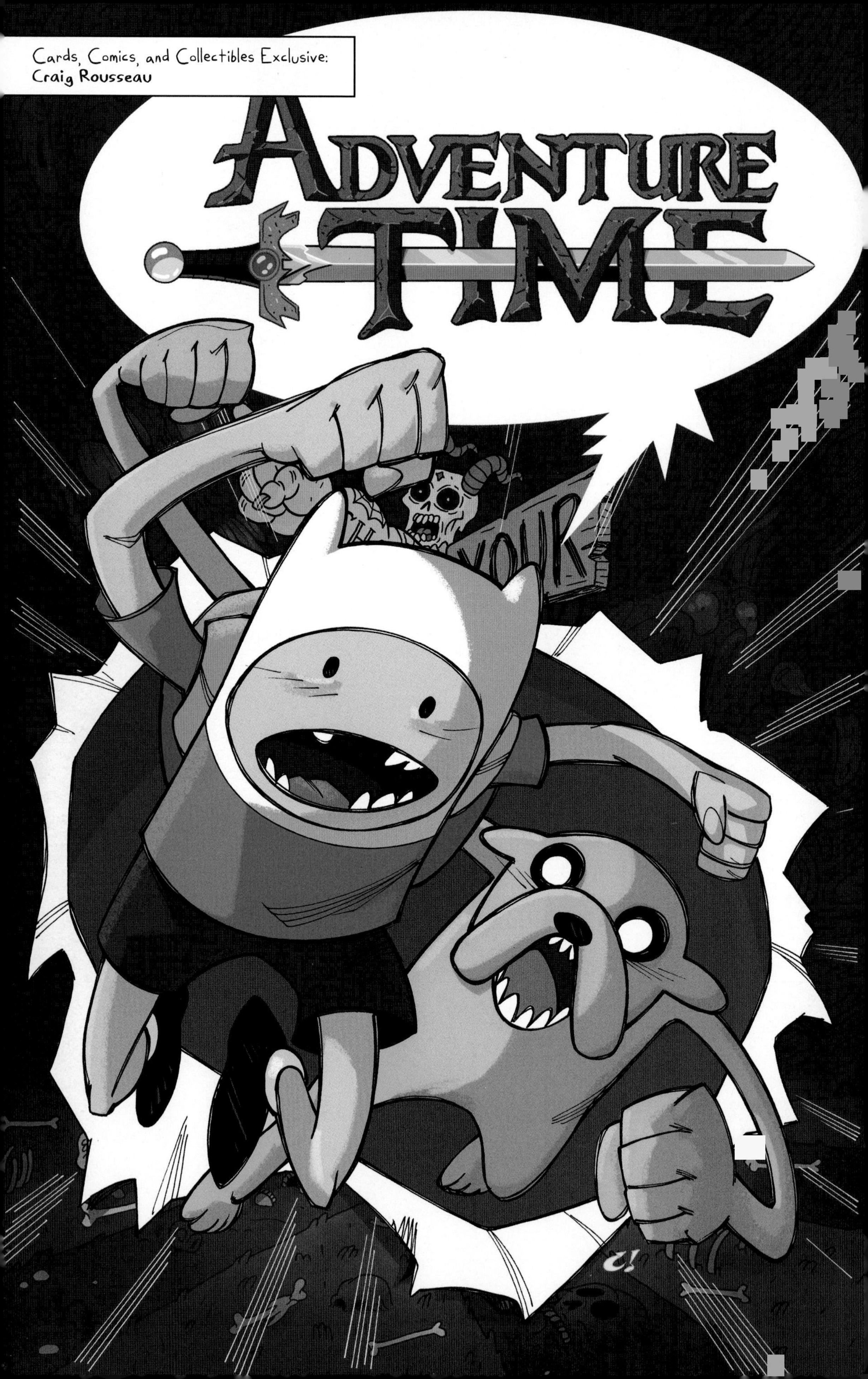

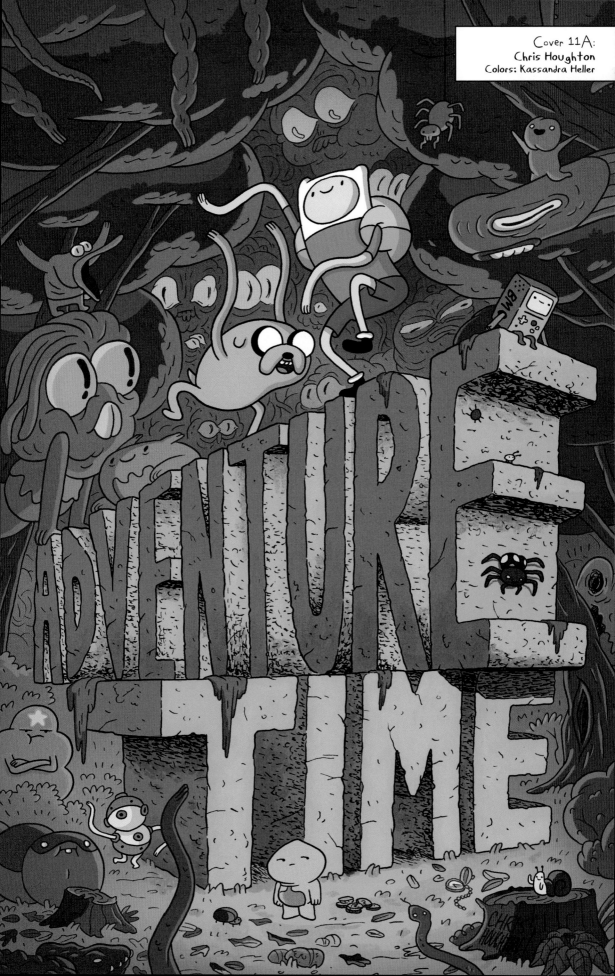

Cover 11B:
Kevin Wada

Cover 12A:
Chris Houghton
Colors: Kassandra Heller

Cover 12C:
Lilli Carré

Cover 12D:
David King

Cover 13B:
Kel McDonald

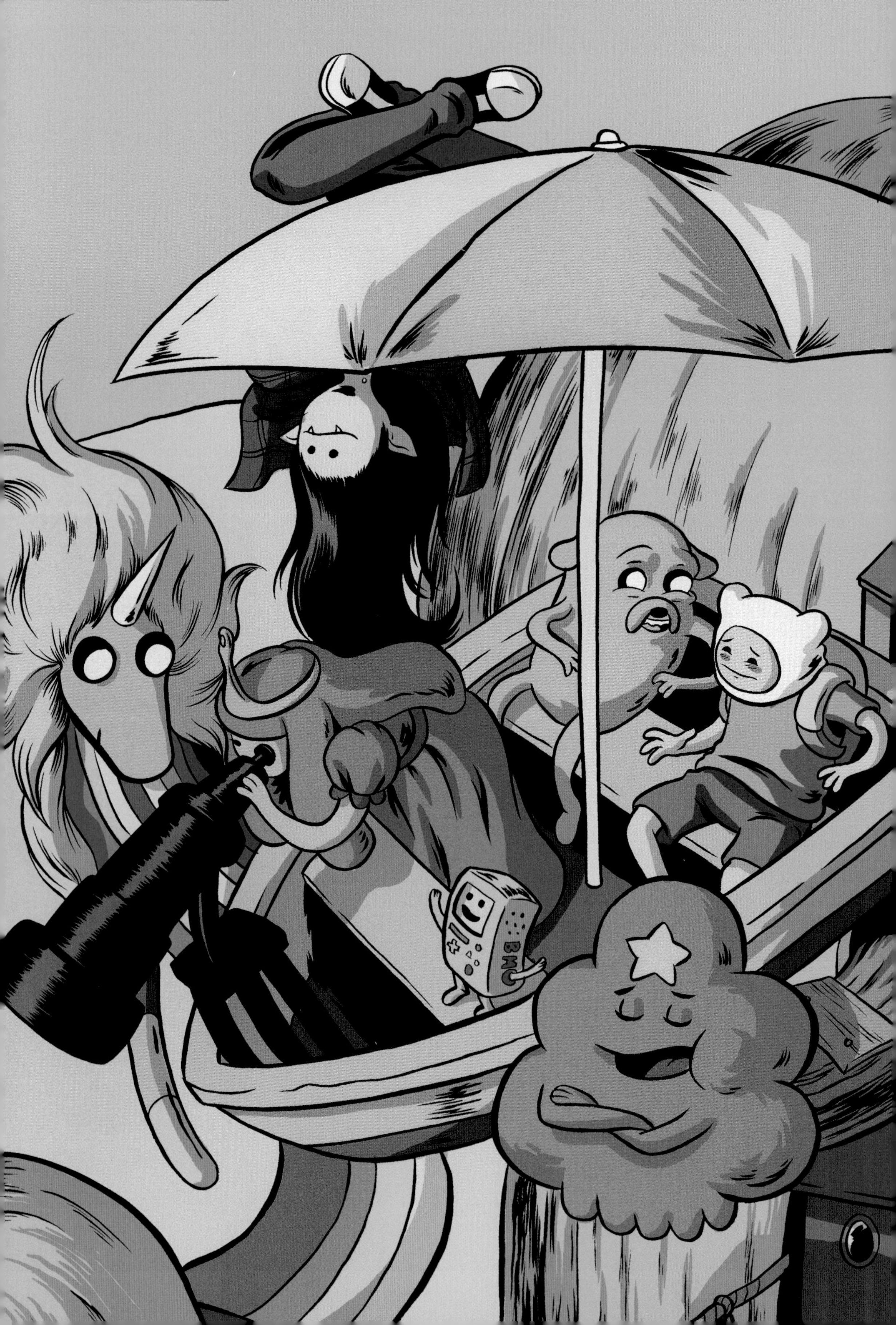

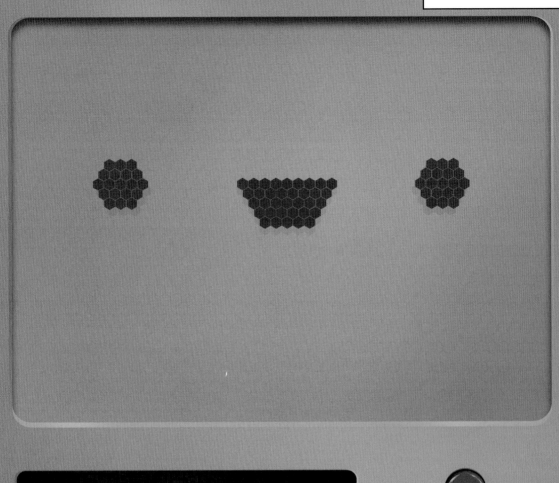

jjwharrison

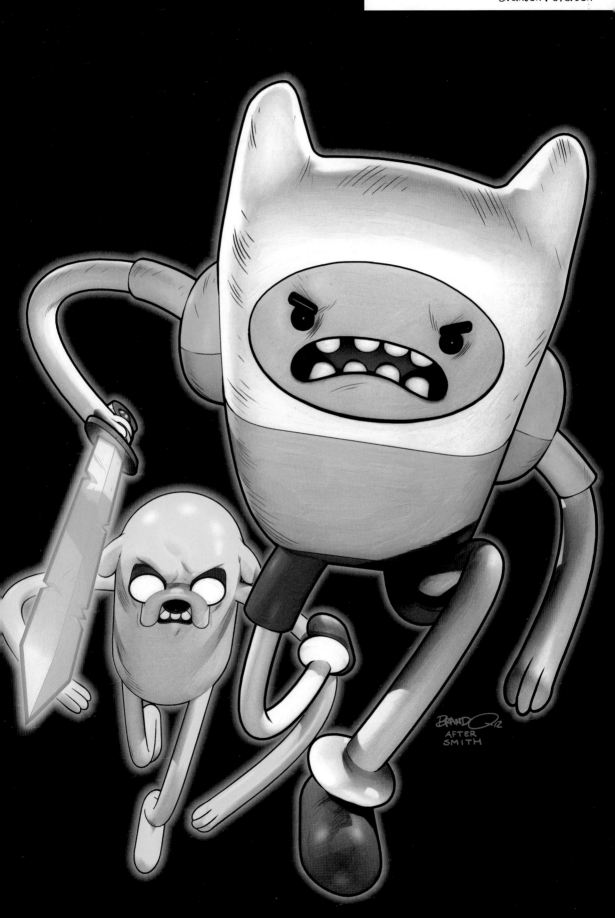

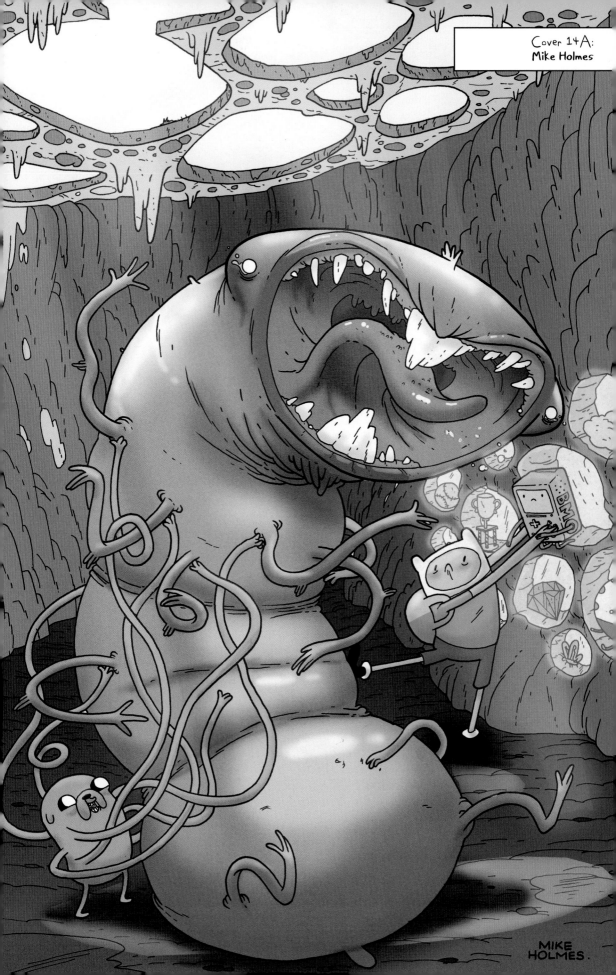

MIKE
HOLMES

Cover 14B:
Jason Ho

Cover 14C:
Liz Prince

Cover 14D:
Ming Doyle

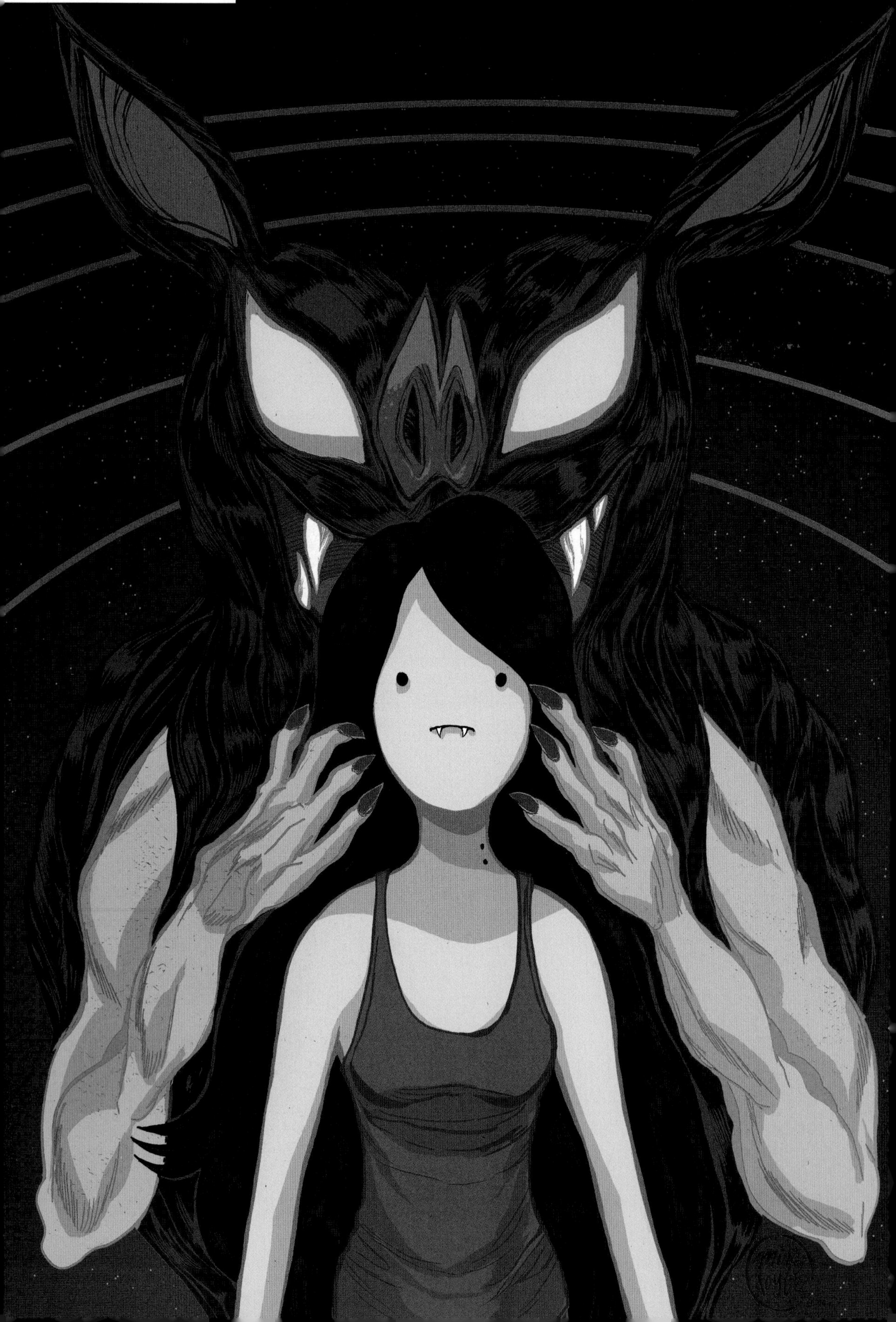